Basic Skills

MULTIPLICATION & DIVISION

for 6 – 7 year olds

Contents

Paul Broadbent

Grouping in twos and threes

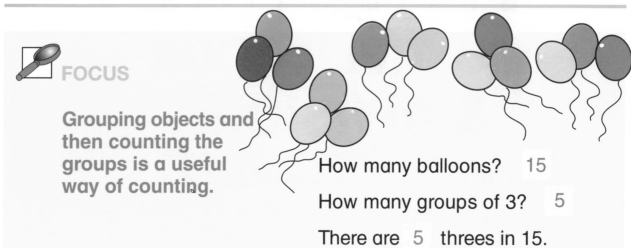

FOCUS

Grouping objects and then counting the groups is a useful way of counting.

How many balloons?   15

How many groups of 3?   5

There are   5   threes in 15.

TRY THESE   **1. Ring these in groups of two.**

hats

groups of 2

sandwiches

groups of 2

2. Ring these in groups of three.

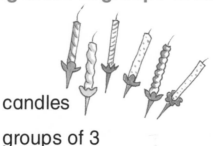

candles

groups of 3

cakes

groups of 3

3 x

3. Draw two cakes on each plate.

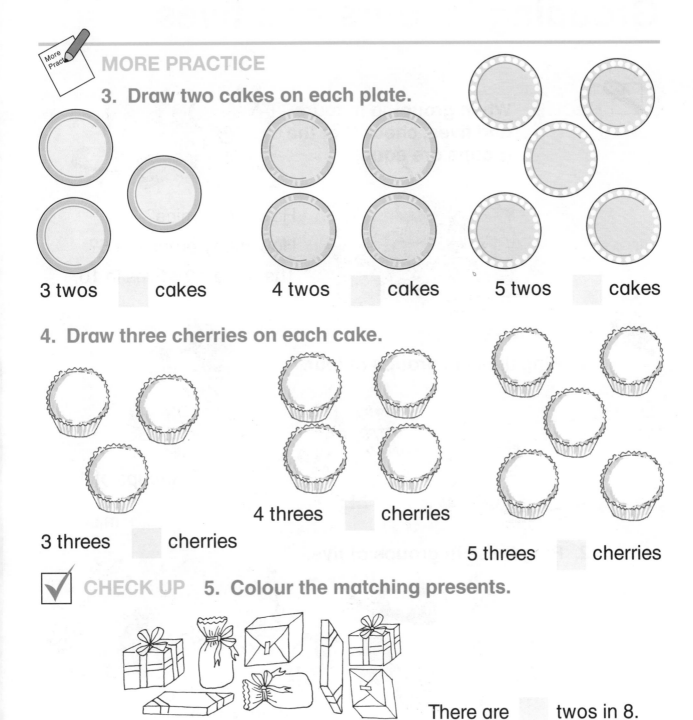

3 twos ☐ cakes   4 twos ☐ cakes   5 twos ☐ cakes

4. Draw three cherries on each cake.

3 threes ☐ cherries

4 threes ☐ cherries

5 threes ☐ cherries

CHECK UP **5. Colour the matching presents.**

There are ☐ twos in 8.

Grouping in fours and fives

FOCUS When grouping in fours and fives, check that the groups are equal.

How many mice? 10

How many groups of 5? 2

There are 2 fives in 10.

TRY THESE

1. Ring these in groups of four.

⬜ groups of 4

⬜ mice

2. Ring these in groups of five.

⬜ groups of 5   ⬜ cats

3. Ring these in groups of four.

_____ groups of four

_____ groups of four

4. Ring these in groups of 5.

_____ groups of five

_____ groups of five

 CHECK UP **5. Use the budgies to help answer these.**

3 groups of 4	5 groups of 3	6 groups of 2
5 groups of 4	2 groups of 10	10 groups of 2

Unit 2

Multiplying by two

FOCUS

Counting in equal groups is also called multiplication. The multiplication sign is ×.

Remember: **3 × 2 gives the same answer as 2 × 3.**

These fish are grouped into twos.

2 + 2 + 2 = 6

3 lots of 2 = 6

3 × 2 = 6

 TRY THESE 1. **Ring these fish in groups of two.**

2 + 2 + 2 + 2 + 2 + 2 =

lots of 2 =

× 2 =

2 + 2 + 2 + 2 + 2 + 2 + 2 =

lots of 2 =

× 2 =

2 + 2 + 2 + 2 =

lots of 2 =

× 2 =

2. **Draw 2 fish in each bowl.**

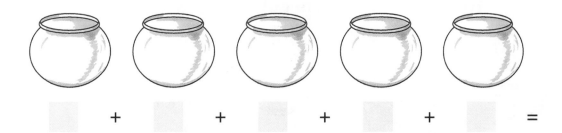

☐ + ☐ + ☐ + ☐ + ☐ = ☐

☐ × 2 = ☐

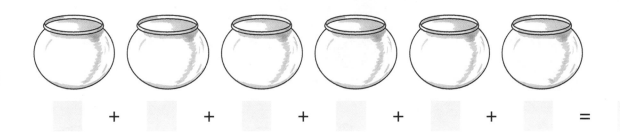

☐ + ☐ + ☐ + ☐ + ☐ = ☐

☐ × 2 = ☐

 CHECK UP 3. **Complete these.**

$1 \times 2 =$ ☐ $\qquad 2 \times 2 =$ ☐ $\qquad 3 \times 2 =$ ☐ $\qquad 4 \times 2 =$ ☐ $\qquad 5 \times 2 =$ ☐

$6 \times 2 =$ ☐ $\qquad 7 \times 2 =$ ☐ $\qquad 8 \times 2 =$ ☐ $\qquad 9 \times 2 =$ ☐ $\qquad 10 \times 2 =$ ☐

Multiplying by three

 FOCUS **Count the groups of three.
This is called multiplication.**

$3 + 3 + 3 + 3 =$ 12

4 lots of 3 =   12

$4 \times 3 =$ 12

 TRY THESE

**1. Group these shells
into threes and answer
the sums.**

$3 + 3 =$

2 lots of 3 =

$2 \times 3 =$

$3 + 3 + 3 + 3 + 3 =$

5 lots of 3 =

$5 \times 3 =$

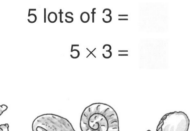

$3 + 3 + 3 + 3 + 3 + 3 =$

6 lots of 3 =

$6 \times 3 =$

Unit 4

2. Draw 3 flags on each castle.

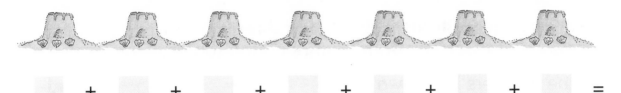

☐ + ☐ + ☐ + ☐ + ☐ + ☐ + ☐ = ☐

☐ × 3 = ☐

☐ + ☐ + ☐ + ☐ + ☐ + ☐ + ☐ + ☐ = ☐

☐ × 3 = ☐

 CHECK UP **3. Complete these.**

$1 \times 3 =$ ☐ $2 \times 3 =$ ☐ $3 \times 3 =$ ☐ $4 \times 3 =$ ☐ $5 \times 3 =$ ☐

$6 \times 3 =$ ☐ $7 \times 3 =$ ☐ $8 \times 3 =$ ☐ $9 \times 3 =$ ☐ $10 \times 3 =$ ☐

Patterns of twos and threes

 FOCUS

2 4 6 8 10 12 14 16 18 20

Learning the patterns of twos and threes is a good way of learning your multiplication tables.

All the numbers in the two times table are even.

3 6 9 12 15 18 21 24 27 30

 TRY THESE 1. Draw jumps of 2.

0 1 2 3 4 5 6 7 8 9 10 11 12 13 14 15 16 17 18 19 20

Write the numbers that you land on.

2. Colour every third number.

1 2 3 4 5 6 7 8 9 10 11 12 13 14 15

16 17 18 19 20 21 22 23 24 25 26 27 28 29 30

Unit 5

3. Write the missing numbers.

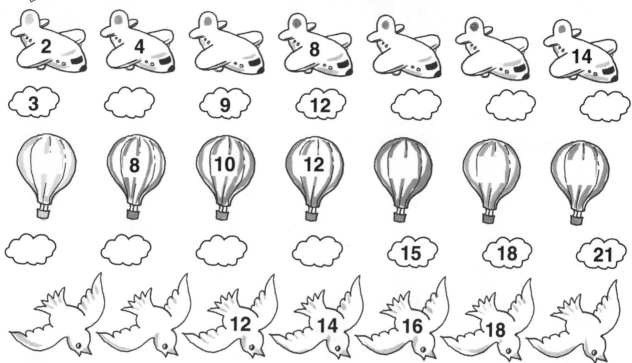

Planes: 2, 4, __, 8, __, __, 14

Clouds: 3, __, 9, 12, __, __, __

Balloons: __, 8, 10, 12, __, __, __

Clouds: __, __, __, __, 15, 18, 21

Birds: __, __, 12, 14, 16, 18, __

✓ CHECK UP 4. Colour all the even numbers.

3	8	14	10	1	6	4	20	11	6	1	17	9	12	3
9	11	6	7	3	18	15	19	7	10	14	13	7	16	5
5	7	12	5	13	14	12	8	3	4	11	18	1	8	19
15	3	20	17	19	4	11	17	5	20	15	13	12	4	1
19	17	2	1	13	6	10	18	19	16	17	11	3	2	13

Which number can you see written?

Patterns of fives and tens

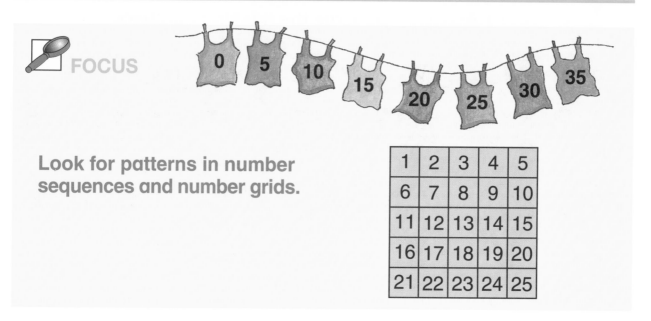

FOCUS

Look for patterns in number
sequences and number grids.

1	2	3	4	5
6	7	8	9	10
11	12	13	14	15
16	17	18	19	20
21	22	23	24	25

TRY THESE   **1.** Continue these patterns.

MORE PRACTICE

2. Colour the numbers in the 5 times table yellow.
Ring the numbers in the 10 times table blue.

What patterns do
you notice?

1	2	3	4	5	6	7	8	9	10
11	12	13	14	15	16	17	18	19	20
21	22	23	24	25	26	27	28	29	30
31	32	33	34	35	36	37	38	39	40
41	42	43	44	45	46	47	48	49	50
51	52	53	54	55	56	57	58	59	60
61	62	63	64	65	66	67	68	69	70
71	72	73	74	75	76	77	78	79	80
81	82	83	84	85	86	87	88	89	90
91	92	93	94	95	96	97	98	99	100

 CHECK UP **3. Complete these grids.**

×	3	2	5
10	30		
5			
2			

×	2	10	5
4			
3			
10			

×	4	5	3
10			
2			
5			

Progress check 1

1. Ring these in groups of two.

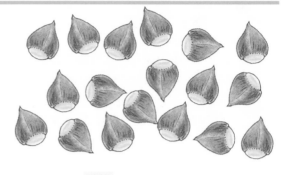

groups of 2

groups of 2

2. Colour these in groups of three.

groups of 3

3. Draw five oranges in each bag.

 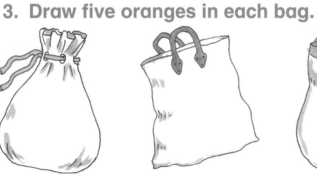  

groups of 5

4. Continue the pattern.

5. Complete these.

$\boxed{} \times 3 = \boxed{}$

$\boxed{} + \boxed{} + \boxed{} = \boxed{}$

$\boxed{} \times 4 = \boxed{}$

$\boxed{} + \boxed{} + \boxed{} + \boxed{} = \boxed{}$

6. Continue the pattern.

0   5   15

7. Complete the grids.

✕	3	5	2
10			
2			
5			

✕	10	3	5
2			
5			
3			

Equal sharing

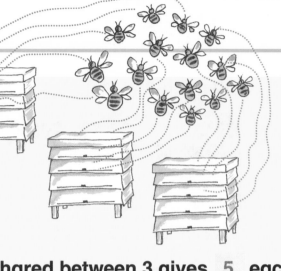

 FOCUS

When sharing it is important to share equally.
These bees are shared equally between three hives.

15 shared between 3 gives 5 each.

 TRY THESE

1. **Share these out equally.**

10 shared between 2
gives ____ each.

15 shared between 5
gives ____ each.

12 shared between 3
gives ____ each.

8 shared between 4 gives ____ each.

MORE PRACTICE

**2. Share these eggs out equally.
Draw them in each nest.**

9 shared by 3

10 shared by 5

8 shared by 2

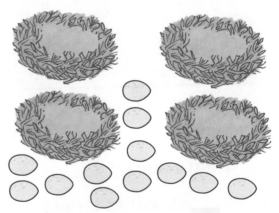

12 shared by 4

 CHECK UP **3. Answer these.**

20 shared by 2

20 shared by 5

20 shared by 10

20 shared by 4

Grouping

 FOCUS

These balls have been grouped in twos.

10 grouped into twos   5   groups

10 divided by 2   5

TRY THESE   **1. Ring these into twos and count the groups.**

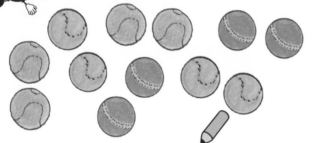

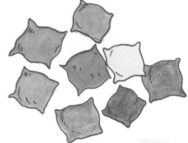

12 grouped into twos   groups   8 grouped into twos   groups

12 divided by 2   8 divided by 2

2. Ring these into threes and count the groups.

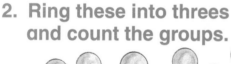

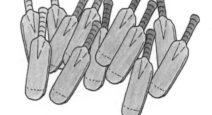

15 grouped into threes   groups   12 grouped into threes   groups

15 divided by 3   12 divided by 3

3. Colour these to show the groups.
   Count the groups.

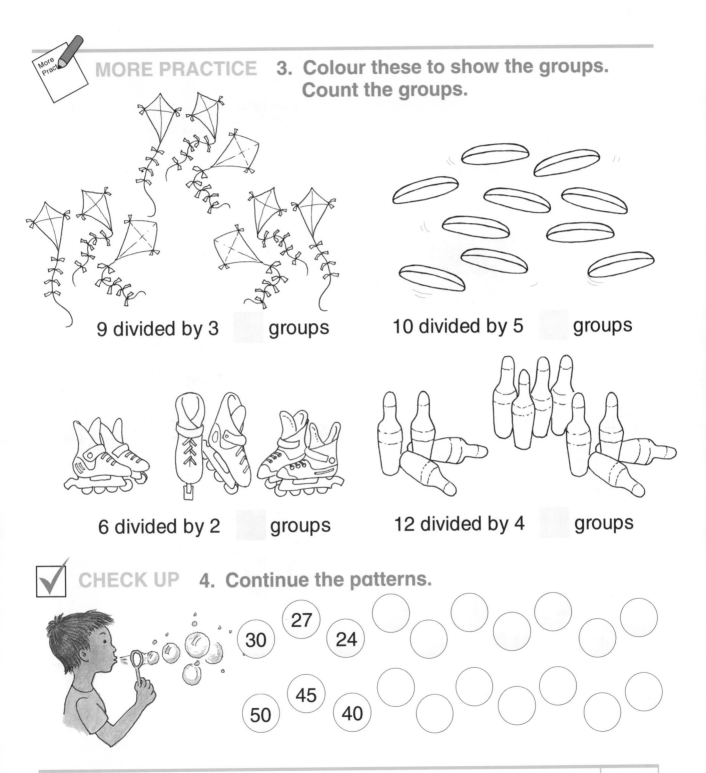

9 divided by 3 [   ] groups

10 divided by 5 [   ] groups

6 divided by 2 [   ] groups

12 divided by 4 [   ] groups

CHECK UP   4. Continue the patterns.

30 27 24

50 45 40

Dividing

FOCUS

Dividing objects can be
shown by grouping them.
The division sign is ÷ .

6 divided by 2 = 3 groups

6 ÷ 2 = 3

TRY THESE   1. How many groups for each of these?

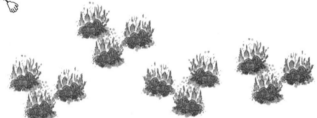

12 divided by 3 =   groups.

8 divided by 2 =   groups.

12 ÷ 3 =

8 ÷ 2 =

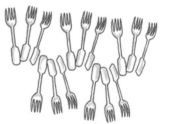

16 divided by 2 =   groups.

15 divided by 3 =   groups.

16 ÷ 2 =

15 ÷ 3 =

2. **Draw 3 cakes on each plate.**
   Complete the sum.

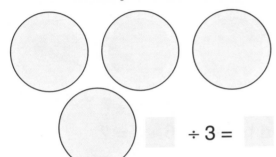

$\square \div 3 = \square$

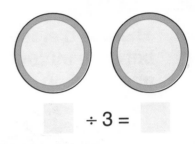

$\square \div 3 = \square$

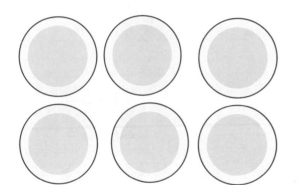

$\square \div 3 = \square$

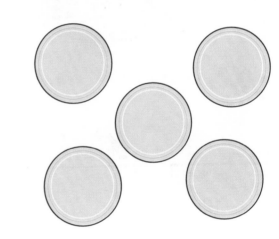

$\square \div 3 = \square$

 CHECK UP

3. **Answer these**
   and colour the
   pattern.

$8 \div 2$

$15 \div 3$

$12 \div 3$

$18 \div 3$

$10 \div 2$

$12 \div 2$

Answer
4 – blue
5 – red
6 – green

Division and multiplication

There is a close link
between multiplication
and division.

2 lots of 3 $\longrightarrow$ $2 \times 3 = 6$
6 divided by 3 $\rightarrow$ $6 \div 3 = 2$

TRY THESE   1. Write the answers.

$4 \times 3 =$

$12 \div 3 =$

$6 \times 2 =$

$12 \div 2 =$

$4 \times 5 =$

$20 \div 5 =$

MORE PRACTICE

2. Write the missing numbers.

$6 \times 3 =$ ____

____ $\div 3 = 6$

$8 \times 2 =$ ____

____ $\div 2 = 8$

$3 \times 5 =$ ____

____ $\div 5 = 3$

$8 \times 3 =$ ____

____ $\div 3 = 8$

$5 \times 5 =$ ____

____ $\div 5 = 5$

$10 \times 2 =$ ____

____ $\div 2 = 10$

$4 \times 10 =$ ____

____ $\div 10 = 4$

$7 \times 3 =$ ____

____ $\div 3 = 7$

$6 \times 10 =$ ____

____ $\div 10 = 6$

 CHECK UP

3. Draw a picture to show:

$5 \times 2 = 10$

and

$10 \div 2 = 5$

Multiplication facts

FOCUS

It is useful to know the × 2, × 5 and × 10 tables by heart. How quickly can you answer these?

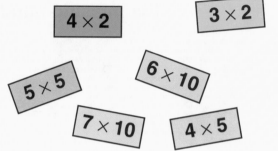

4 × 2

3 × 2

6 × 10

5 × 5

7 × 10

4 × 5

TRY THESE

1. Complete these and learn the facts.

×2			×5			×10	

×2	×5	×10
1 × 2 =	1 × 5 =	1 × 10 =
2 × 2 =	2 × 5 =	2 × 10 =
3 × 2 =	3 × 5 =	3 × 10 =
4 × 2 =	4 × 5 =	4 × 10 =
5 × 2 =	5 × 5 =	5 × 10 =
6 × 2 =	6 × 5 =	6 × 10 =
7 × 2 =	7 × 5 =	7 × 10 =
8 × 2 =	8 × 5 =	8 × 10 =
9 × 2 =	9 × 5 =	9 × 10 =
10 × 10 =	10 × 10 =	10 × 10 =

2. **Match each frog to a lily pad.**

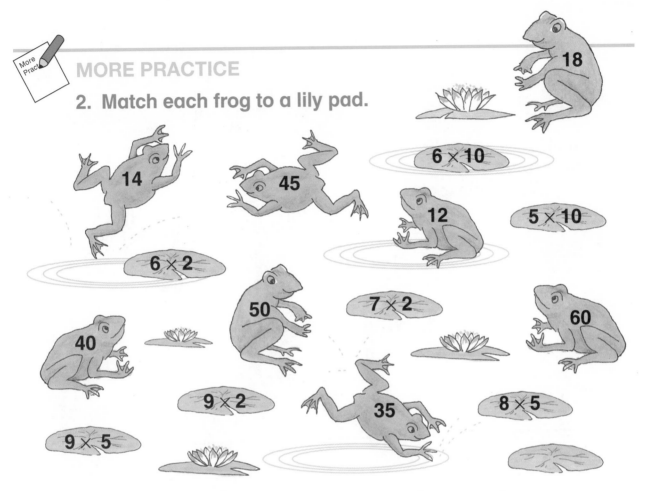

Write a sum on the spare lily pad for the extra frog.

 CHECK UP 3. **Time yourself answering these. Use a separate piece of paper. Repeat and try to beat your best time.**

a. 4×2	**b.** 3×5	**c.** 5×5	**d.** 6×10	**e.** 8×2
f. 2×10	**g.** 9×2	**h.** 6×5	**i.** 3×10	**j.** 7×2
k. 10×10	**l.** 5×10	**m.** 2×2	**n.** 8×5	**o.** 7×5
p. 8×10	**q.** 5×2	**r.** 3×2	**s.** 9×10	**t.** 7×10

Unit 11

Division facts

8×2 $16 \div 2$ 10×10 $100 \div 10$ $15 \div 3$ 3×5

FOCUS

It is useful to know the
division facts ÷ 2, ÷ 5
and ÷ 10. The table facts
will help you.

 TRY THESE   1. Write the answers.

÷ 2	÷ 5	÷ 10
2 ÷ 2 =	5 ÷ 5 =	10 ÷ 10 =
4 ÷ 2 =	10 ÷ 5 =	20 ÷ 10 =
6 ÷ 2 =	15 ÷ 5 =	30 ÷ 10 =
8 ÷ 2 =	20 ÷ 5 =	40 ÷ 10 =
10 ÷ 2 =	25 ÷ 5 =	50 ÷ 10 =
12 ÷ 2 =	30 ÷ 5 =	60 ÷ 10 =
14 ÷ 2 =	35 ÷ 5 =	70 ÷ 10 =
16 ÷ 2 =	40 ÷ 5 =	80 ÷ 10 =
18 ÷ 2 =	45 ÷ 5 =	90 ÷ 10 =
20 ÷ 2 =	50 ÷ 5 =	100 ÷ 10 =

MORE PRACTICE

**2. Work out the answers.
Use the code to find the fruit.
Draw the fruit in the boxes.**

1	S
2	A
3	L
4	P
5	G
6	E
7	B
8	N
9	R
10	T

$8 \div 2 =$ ___ P

$12 \div 2 =$ ___

$4 \div 2 =$ ___

$18 \div 2 =$ ___

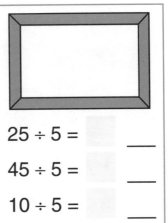

$25 \div 5 =$ ___

$45 \div 5 =$ ___

$10 \div 5 =$ ___

$20 \div 5 =$ ___

$30 \div 5 =$ ___

$70 \div 10 =$ ___

$20 \div 10 =$ ___

$40 \div 5 =$ ___

$4 \div 2 =$ ___

$80 \div 10 =$ ___

$10 \div 5 =$ ___

$10 \div 5 =$ ___

$40 \div 10 =$ ___

$8 \div 2 =$ ___

$30 \div 10 =$ ___

$12 \div 2 =$ ___

 **CHECK UP   3. Time yourself to answer these. Write the
answers on paper. Repeat and try to beat your best time.**

a.	$20 \div 5$	**b.**	$18 \div 2$	**c.**	$30 \div 10$	**d.**	$6 \div 2$	**e.**	$12 \div 2$
f.	$35 \div 5$	**g.**	$15 \div 5$	**h.**	$8 \div 2$	**i.**	$50 \div 10$	**j.**	$45 \div 5$
k.	$90 \div 10$	**l.**	$10 \div 2$	**m.**	$100 \div 10$	**n.**	$40 \div 5$	**o.**	$14 \div 2$
p.	$50 \div 5$	**q.**	$16 \div 2$	**r.**	$40 \div 10$	**s.**	$10 \div 5$	**t.**	$20 \div 2$

✔ Progress check 2

1. Share these out equally.

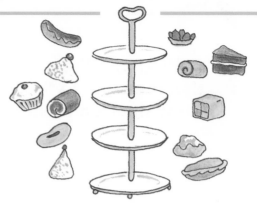

15 shared by 3 ⟶ ▢   12 shared by 4 ⟶ ▢

2. Colour these to show the groups.

10 divided by 2 ⟶ ▢   15 divided by 5 ⟶ ▢

3. Answer these.

$4 \times 2 =$ ▢ $7 \times 5 =$ ▢ $9 \times 10 =$ ▢

▢ $\div 2 = 4$ ▢ $\div 5 = 7$ ▢ $\div 10 = 9$

4. Complete these so that they equal the star number.

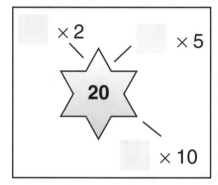
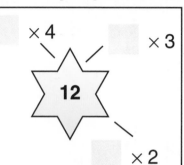
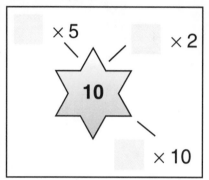

5, Draw lines to match the answers.

6. Answer these.

$5 \times 10 =$ $7 \times 2 =$ $9 \times 5 =$ $8 \times 10 =$

$16 \div 2 =$ $20 \div 10 =$ $40 \div 5 =$ $18 \div 2 =$

Answers

Unit 1

1. 8   12
   4   6
2. 6   18
   2   6
3. 6   8   10
4. 9   12   15
5. See colouring.
   4

Unit 2

1. 3   12
2. 3   15
3. 2   4
4. 4   5
5. 12   15   12
   20   20   20

Unit 3

1.   12
   6   12
   6   12
          14
   7   14
   7   14
          8
   4   8
   4   8
2. $2 + 2 + 2 + 2 + 2 = 10$
   $5 \times 2 = 10$
   $2 + 2 + 2 + 2 + 2 + 2 = 12$
   $6 \times 2 = 12$
3. 2   4   6   8   10
   12   14   16   18   20

Unit 4

1. 6
   6
   6
   15
   15
   15
   18
   18
   18
2. $3 + 3 + 3 + 3 + 3 + 3 + 3 = 21$
   $7 \times 3 = 21$
   $3 + 3 + 3 + 3 + 3 + 3 + 3 + 3 = 24$
   $8 \times 3 = 24$
3. 3   6   9   12   15
   18   21   24   27   30

Unit 5

1. 2 4 6 8 10 12 14 16 18 20
2. 3 6 9 12 15 18 21 24 27 30
3. 2   4   6   8   10   12   14
   3   6   9   12   15   18   21
   6   8   10   12   14   16   18
   3   6   9   12   15   18   21
   8   10   12   14   16   18   20
4. You can see the word **TEN**.

Unit 6

1. 10 20 30 40 50 60 70 80
     0   5 10 15 20 25 30 35
   80 70 60 50 40 30 20 10
   50 45 40 35 30 25 20 15
2. See number square.
3. 30 20 50   8 40 20   40 50 30
   15 10 25   6 30 15   8 10 15
     6   4 10   20 100 50   20 25 15

Progress check 1

1. 7   9
2. 5
3. 4
4. 0 10 20 30 40 50 60 70
5. $5 + 5 + 5 = 15$
   $5 \times 3 = 15$
   $3 + 3 + 3 + 3 = 12$
   $3 \times 4 = 12$
6. 0 5 10 15 20 25 30 35 40
7. 30   50   20   20   30   50
     6   10   4   50   15   25
   15   25   10   30   9   15

Unit 7

1. 5   3
   4   2
2. 3   2
   4   3
3. 10   4
   2   5

Unit 8

1. 6   4
   6   4
2. 5   4
   5   4
3. 3   2
   3   3
4. 30 27 24 21 18 15 12 9 6 3
   50 45 40 35 30 25 20 15 10 5

Unit 9

1. 4   4
   4   4

   8   5
   8   5

2. 12   4   6   2
   18   6   15   5

3. See colouring:
   blue – $12 \div 3$; $8 \div 2$
   red – $10 \div 2$; $15 \div 3$
   green – $18 \div 3$; $12 \div 2$

Unit 10

1. 12   12   20
    4   6   4

2. 18   16   15
   18   16   15

   24   25   20
   24   25   20

   40   21   60
   40   21   60

3. Check child's drawing.

Unit 11

1.   2   5   10
     4   10   20
     6   15   30
     8   20   40
   10   25   50
   12   30   60
   14   35   70
   16   40   90
   20   50   100

2. $6 \times 2 = 12$, $6 \times 10 = 60$,
   $9 \times 5 = 45$, $9 \times 2 = 18$,
   $7 \times 2 = 14$, $8 \times 5 = 40$,
   $5 \times 10 = 50$

   The spare lily pad should be
   5×7 or 7×5.

3. **a.** 8   **b.** 15   **c.** 25
   d. 60   **e.** 16   **f.** 20
   g. 18   **h.** 30   **i.** 30
   j. 14   **k.** 100   **l.** 50
   m. 4   **n.** 40   **o.** 35
   p. 80   **q.** 10   **r.** 6
   s. 90   **t.** 70

Unit 12

1. 1   1   1
    2   2   2
    3   3   3
    4   4   4
    5   5   5
    6   6   6
    7   7   7
    8   8   8
    9   9   9
   10   10   10

2. 4   P   5   G
   6   E   9   R
   2   A   2   A
   9   R   4   P
               6   E

   7   B   2   A
   2   A   4   P
   8   N   4   P
   2   A   3   L
   8   N   6   E
   2   A

3. **a.** 4   **b.** 9   **c.** 3   **d.** 3   **e.** 6
   f. 7   **g.** 3   **h.** 4   **i.** 5   **j.** 9
   k. 9   **l.** 5   **m.** 10   **n.** 8   **o.** 7
   p. 10   **q.** 8   **r.** 4   **s.** 2   **t.** 10

Progress check 2

1. 5   3

2. 5   3

3. 8   35   90
   8   35   90

4. 10, 4, 2   3, 4, 6   2, 5, 1

5. $18 \div 2 = 9$ $35 \div 5 = 7$
   $80 \div 8 = 10$ $12 \div 2 = 6$
   $25 \div 5 = 5$

6. 50   14   45   80
    8   2   8   9

Answers

Record sheet

How easy did you find it?

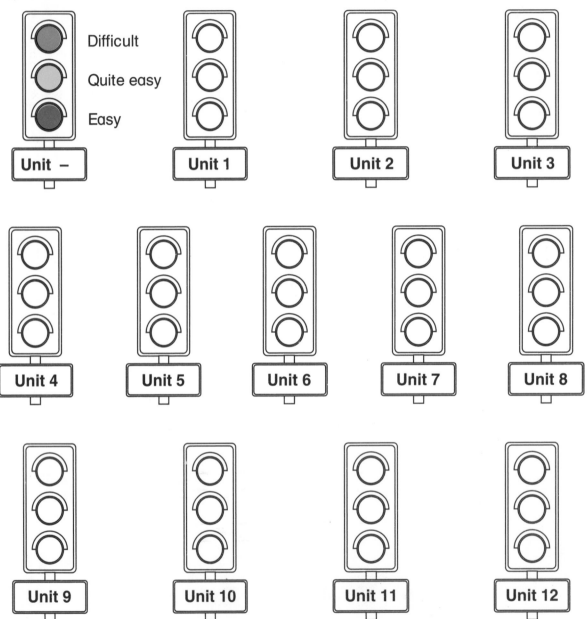

Difficult

Quite easy

Easy

Unit –

Unit 1

Unit 2

Unit 3

Unit 4

Unit 5

Unit 6

Unit 7

Unit 8

Unit 9

Unit 10

Unit 11

Unit 12